W9-BLS-759

May I Come In?

Theodore Clymer

Patricia Miles Martin
Doris Gates

Consultants

William E. Blanton EVALUATION
Milton D. Jacobson READABILITY
Ken Johnson LANGUAGE
Roger W. Shuy LINGUISTICS
E. Paul Torrance CREATIVITY

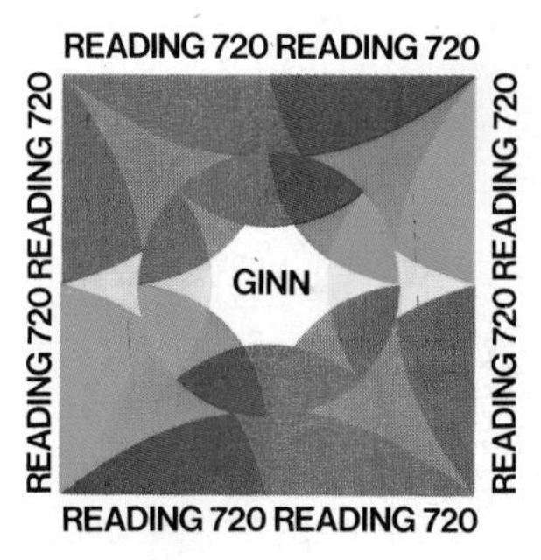

GINN AND COMPANY
A Xerox Education Company

Acknowledgments

Grateful acknowledgment is made to the following publishers, authors, and agents for permission to use and adapt copyrighted materials:

Grosset & Dunlap, Inc., for "Mr. Pine's Signs" and "The Mixed-Up Signs." Adapted from *Mr. Pine's Mixed-Up Signs* by Leonard Kessler. Copyright © 1961 by Wonder Books, Inc. Published by Grosset & Dunlap, Inc.

Harcourt Brace Jovanovich, Inc., for the poem "Buildings" by Myra Cohn Livingston from *Whispers and Other Poems,* © 1958 by Myra Cohn Livingston. Reprinted by permission of Harcourt Brace Jovanovich, Inc.

Jack and Jill Magazine for "Mr. Big," adapted from "The Old Man and His Farm" by Edna Geries. Adapted by permission of *Jack and Jill* Magazine. Copyright 1964, The Saturday Evening Post Company, Inc.

J. B. Lippincott Company for the poem "About the Teeth of Sharks" from *You Read to Me, I'll Read to You* by John Ciardi. Copyright © 1962 by John Ciardi. Reprinted by permission of J. B. Lippincott Company.

University of California Press for the poem beginning "Quickly fly away" by Issa, from *The Year of My Life:* A Translation of Issa's Oraga Haru by Nobuyuki Yuasa. Originally published by the University of California Press; reprinted by permission of The Regents of the University of California.

Western Publishing Company, Inc., for "Bozo," adapted from *Too Many Bozos* by Lilian Moore, © Copyright 1960 by Western Publishing Company, Inc. Also for *Home for a Bunny* by Margaret Wise Brown, © Copyright 1956, 1961 by Western Publishing Company, Inc. Both used by permission of the publisher.

Illustrations and photographs were provided by the following: Kathy Arnold (100-103); Willi Baum (171-191); Alan Blank/Bruce Coleman Inc. (35); Mick Church (32); Lydia Dabcovich (192-199); Len Ebert (126-135); Lois Ehlert (104-105, 166-170, 200-201); Les Gray (137-143, 154-161, 82, 83, 122, 123, 162, 163, 203); Owen Franklin/Stock Boston (136); James Karales/Peter Arnold (25); John Kuzich (86-92, 106-112, 120-121); David Muench/Van Cleve Photography (36-37); Josef Muench (38-41); Bill Morrison (144-150); Leslie Morrill (8-15); Lucinda McQueen (16-23, 42-43); Joan Paley (77); Jan Palmer (46-59, 68-74); Hans Reinhart/Bruce Coleman (33); Photo Researchers Inc. (26); Leonard Lee Rue/Bruce Coleman Inc. (24); James Simon/Bruce Coleman Inc. (34); Lynn Sweat (27-31); George Ulrich (152-153); Joseph Veno (78-81); Jean Winslow (204-221); Fred Witzig (93-99).

The cover and unit introduction pages were designed by Gregory Fossella Associates.

PARTS OF THIS WORK WERE PUBLISHED IN THE GINN *READING 360* PROGRAM.

HOME OFFICE: LEXINGTON, MASSACHUSETTS 02173
0-663-30693-0

Contents

Unit 5 OLD TALES TO TELL

BOOK-LENGTH STORY

A Bit of Leaf - A Bit of Weed

The Fox

The fox is looking
for something to eat.

A little rabbit is looking
for a bit of something to eat.

He is looking for a bit of leaf—
a bit of weed.

Here comes the fox!
But the rabbit gets away.

Near a big log,
a mouse is looking
for something to eat.

The fox sees the mouse
near the log.

Here comes the fox!

But the mouse runs under the log.

The fox is looking
for a fine, big hen.

Here comes a *DOG!*

And away the fox runs—
away—
away—
away.

The Mouse and the Snowman

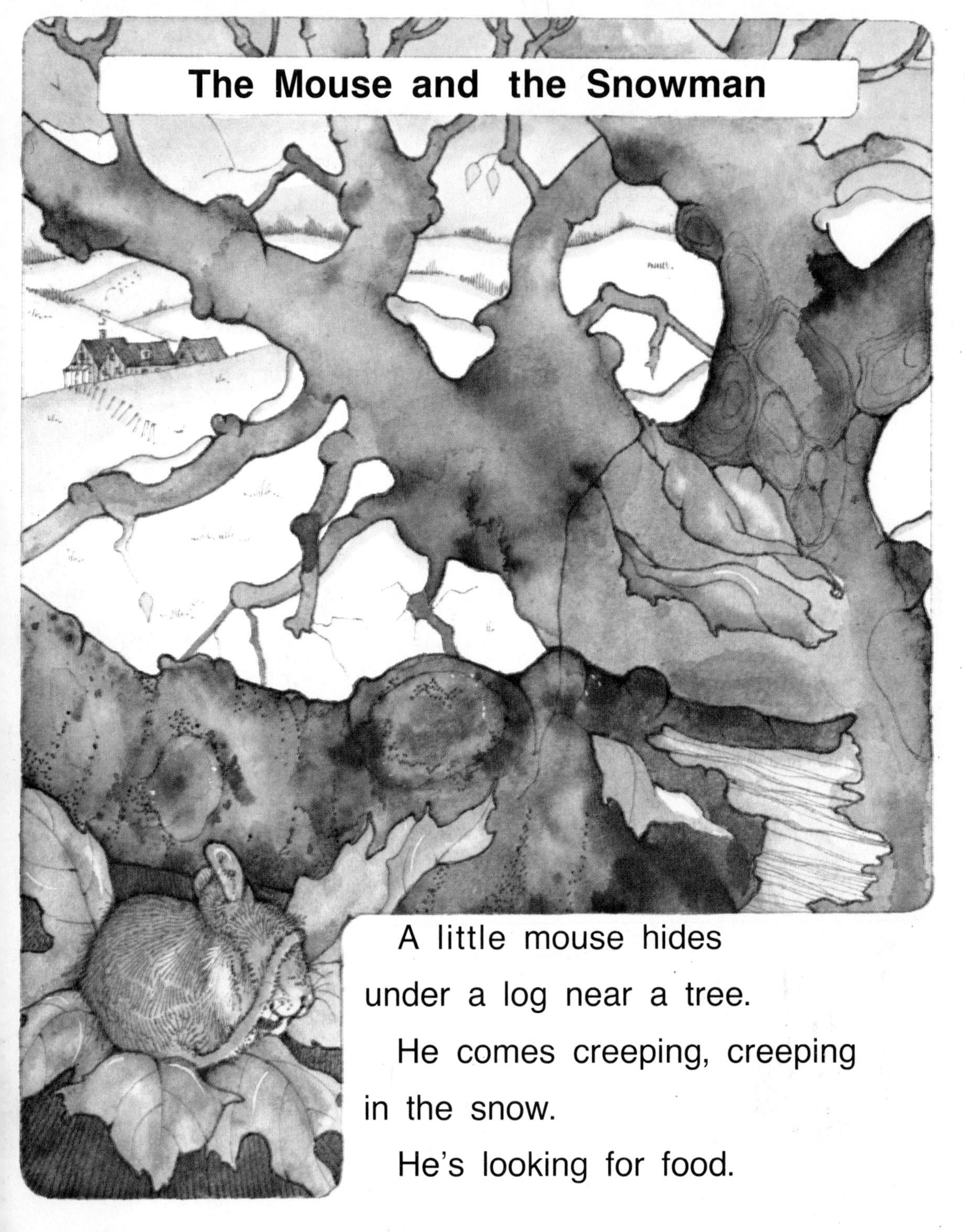

A little mouse hides
under a log near a tree.

He comes creeping, creeping
in the snow.

He's looking for food.

And what can he find in the snow?

No food!

Not a bit!

Not a bite!

The little mouse sees something.
He runs away
and hides in the snow.

The little mouse is looking!

He sees a snowman near the log under the tree.

And he sees a girl and a boy.

The girl and the boy go away.

The little mouse comes—
creeping—creeping—
looking for food.

He runs—looking—looking.

He runs to the snowman.

What can he find?

The little mouse can find food!
Bits and bits of gingerbread.
He eats and eats.

He sits under the tree.

And he washes his face
and his feet.

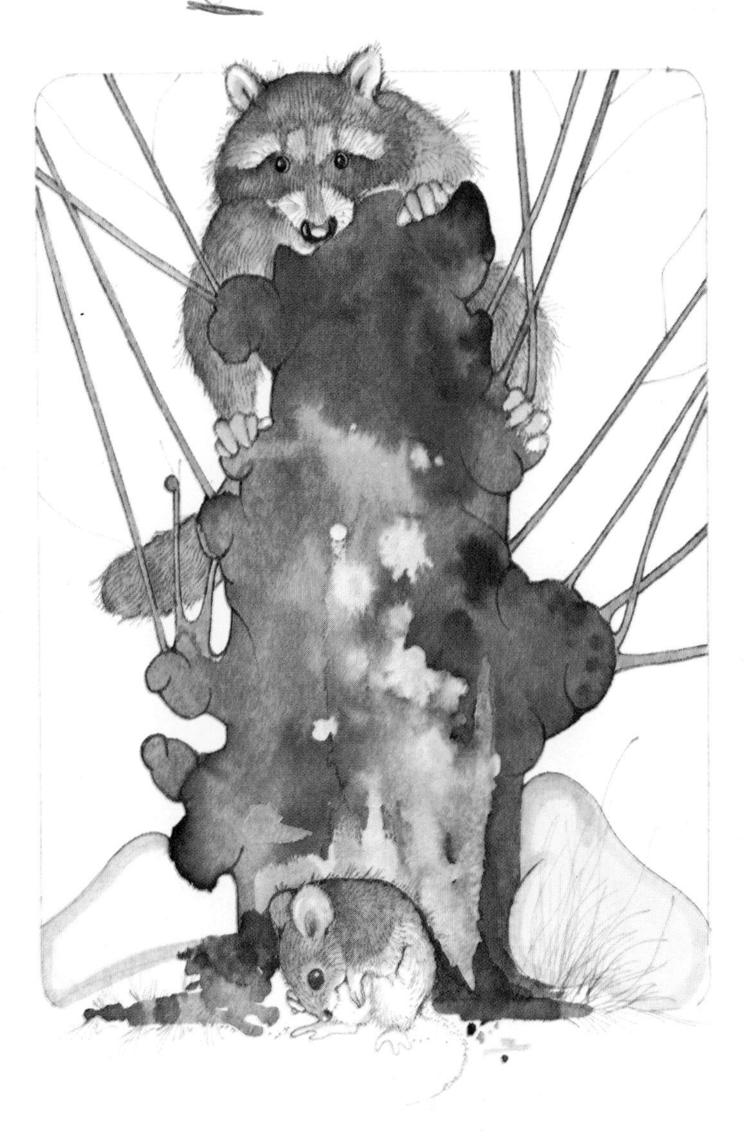

The Raccoons

Little raccoons live
in this home.

They live with the mother raccoon.

The little raccoons can't see.

They can't play.

They are too little to live
away from home.

Now the little raccoons can see.

Now they can play.

And they can go away from home.

They follow the mother raccoon.

The little raccoons go
down the tree.

Down they go with the mother raccoon.

They follow the mother raccoon
away from the tree.

The little raccoons like to play.

They run up and down—
up and down!

Now the little raccoons will go home.

They follow the mother raccoon up the tree.

TRACKS in the Snow

What animal ran
up the hill in the snow?

Follow the tracks,
and you will know.

What animal ran
on the hill
in the snow?

Follow the tracks,
and you will know.

What animal ran
down the hill
in the snow?

Follow the tracks,
and you will know.

Who made the tracks?
Who made the tracks?
Who made the tracks
you see on the snow?

Look in the homes.
Look in the homes.
Look in the homes
and you will know.

Animals in Danger

Animals can hide from danger.

Squirrel runs up a tree.

Raccoon hides in a tree too.

Fox hides in a den.

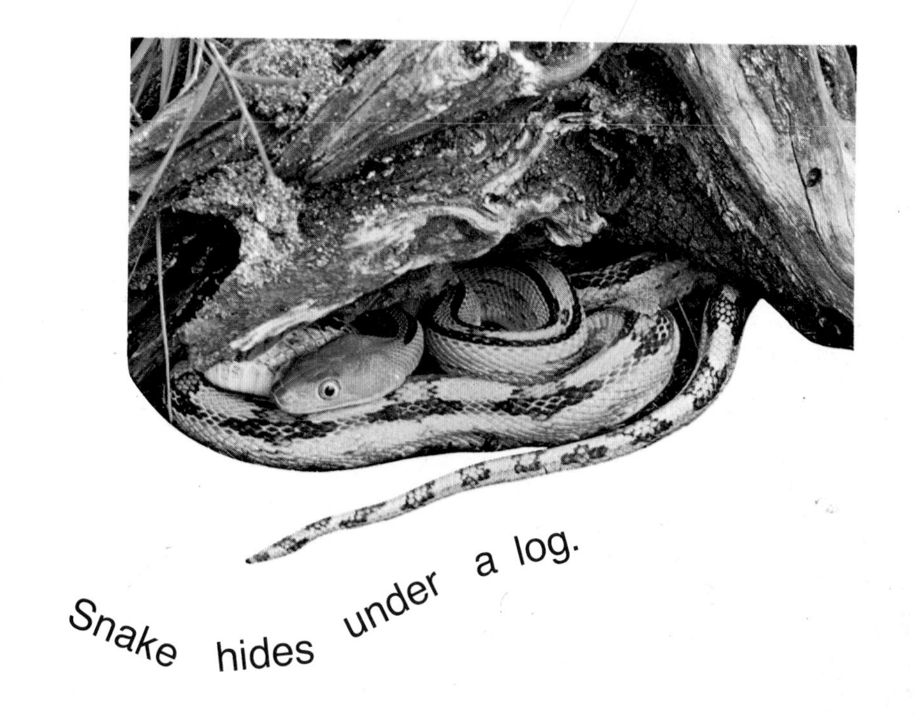

Snake hides under a log.

And turtle hides too!

The Desert

The sun comes up.

It is time to take the sheep from the night pen.

It is time to see the beauty of the desert.

It is time to see the beauty
of the day.

The sun sets.

It is time to take the sheep back to the night pen.

It is time to see the beauty of the night.

Follow the Tracks
rabbit tracks
raccoon tracks
fox tracks
Kim's tracks

Did the raccoon go near the fox's home?

Did the rabbit go up a hill?

Did the rabbit go near the fox's home?

Did Kim follow the raccoon?

Did the fox follow Kim?

Did the fox follow the raccoon?

Did Kim go near the fox's home?

Did the fox go to Kim's home?

City Places

New Boots

James said, " I want new boots. Do you have boots for boys? "

" Yes, we do, " said the man. " Come with me, and you can see what we have. "

James looked at boots for boys.
His mother looked at the boots too.

" Here are the boots I want, "
James said.
" Will you get the boots for me? "

" Yes, I will, "
said his mother.

Penny looked at the boots.

"Will you get new boots for me too?" she said.

"No, Penny," said Mother. "The boots you have aren't old. You don't need new boots now."

The man looked at James.
" Here is a balloon for you, " he said.
" The balloon comes with the boots. "

" Thank you, " said James.

James looked at Penny.
" I have new boots, " he said.
" Do you want this balloon? "

" Yes, I do, " said Penny.
" Now I have something new too.
Thank you, James. Thank you. "

The Red Balloon

James said,

" I like my new boots. "

Penny said,

" I like my red balloon too. "

" Don't play with the balloon
in here, " said Mother.
" You can play with it at home. "

James and his mother went on.
They didn't see where Penny went.

" Hello, little dog, "
said Penny.
" Do you like my red balloon? "

Away went the dog with her balloon.
Penny said, " Stop! Stop!
Where are you going with my balloon? "

A woman said, " Stop, Jet.
Here, Jet! Here, Jet! "

Jet ran on and on.

Penny said, " My balloon!
The dog can't have it. "

The woman went to find Jet.
But she didn't know
where to look for her dog.

"The woman is looking for the balloon,"
said Mother.
"She wants to get it for you."

"She's not going to get the balloon,"
said Penny.
"She wants her dog.
But I want my red balloon."

Where Is Jet ?

Mother and James went with Penny to look for Jet.

But they didn't see the little dog.

A man asked, " Are you looking for something? "

" Yes, we are, " said Penny.

" We are looking for a dog with a red balloon. "

" A dog? " asked the man.

" A dog with a balloon? "

" Can you help find the dog? "
asked Penny.

" We don't know where he went. "

" I know! " said James.

" Look, Mother.

I see Jet. "

The woman saw Jet too.

But Penny saw the balloon.
She said, " My balloon! Oh! Oh!
Now I can't play with it. "

Mother looked at Penny.
" We can get a new balloon, Penny, "
she said.

" We have some animal balloons, "
said the man.

" Some animal balloons! " said Penny.
" I like animal balloons. "

The woman asked, " May I get
a balloon for Penny? "

Penny looked at the animal balloons.
She saw some rabbit balloons
and a parrot balloon.
She saw red and purple balloons.

She looked at the big,
purple parrot balloon.

The woman looked at Penny.
" Do you want the purple balloon? "
she asked.
" You may have it. "

" Oh, thank you, " said Penny.
"Now I have a parrot.
And you have Jet. "

Pigeons and Popcorn

Toni looked up at the big buildings.

Pigeons came down from the buildings, looking for food.

A woman came down the street.
" Are you lost? " she said to Toni.
" You're not lost, are you? "

" No. " Toni said.
" My sister is going to meet me here.
I'm not lost. "

The woman went down the street.

Mike Park came up the street
eating popcorn.
" Hi, Toni, " he said.

And the popcorn fell
at his feet.

Popcorn! Popcorn!

The pigeons came down from the buildings.

Pigeons—pigeons—looking for something to eat!

“ Get away, ” Mike said.
“ Get away from me.
Get away from my popcorn! ”

Toni ran to help.
" Come on, Mike, " she said.
" We have to get away from the pigeons.
Come on with me. "

Mike went up the street with Toni.
They came to a stop
and looked back at the pigeons.
They saw the pigeons
eating the popcorn in the street.

" Here's my sister, " Toni said.

" I have something for you, "
her sister said.
" And something for Mike too—
a big bag of popcorn! "

Toni looked at the pigeons.
" Now the pigeons have popcorn
and we do too! "

ISABEL

" You can't guess where we are going, "
said David Yee.
" It's going to be a surprise. "

" I like surprises, "
said Isabel.

" I'll let you guess
where we are all going, "
said David.

" Are we going to the zoo? " asked Pete.
" We went to the zoo, " said Penny.

" That is not where we are going, "
said David.

" Are we going to the airport? " asked Ken.
" We went to the airport, " said Dan.

" I want to go up in *that* building, "
said Isabel.

" That is not where we are going, "
said David.

“This is where we are going,” said David.
“And here we are.”

“A fire truck!” said Isabel.

“And a fire fighter,”
said Ken.

Then a fire fighter let all the boys and girls get on the truck.

Up they went on the fire truck.

They looked everywhere on the fire truck.

Then they came down and looked everywhere under the truck.

" Who wants to try on my hat? "
the fire fighter asked.

" Let me try it on, " said Ken.
" Me too, " said Pete.
" Me! " said Isabel.

The boys and girls looked everywhere.
And David looked everywhere too.

Then David said, "Time to go."

"But we are not all here," said Dan.
"Who's not here?"

"It's Isabel," said Penny.
"She's lost," said Pete.

"My hat seems to be lost too,"
the fire fighter said.

"Isabel can't be lost!"
David said.
"Look for her! All of you!"

The fire fighter looked too.

" Here she is, " the fire fighter said.
" And here's my hat! "

" Come down now, Isabel, "
said David.
" It's time to go. "

Isabel came down.

" Time to go, "
said David.

" O.K., " said Isabel.
" But I'll be back! "

Buildings *Myra Cohn Livingston*

Buildings are a great surprise,
Every one's a different size.
Offices
Grow
long
and
high,
tall
enough
to
touch
the
sky.

Houses
seem
more like a box,
made of glue
and building blocks.
Every time you look,
you see
Buildings
shaped quite
differently.

Old Buildings and New

Men are at work here.
Some old buildings have to come down.

The men work with big machines.
Men and machines are everywhere.
Down come the old buildings.

Now the old buildings are down,
and new buildings are going up.

Men work with machines here too.

Up go the new buildings.

Men work to finish
the new buildings.

They work with machines.

Now men and machines will go away.

And who will come here to live?

Is This in a City?

elephants and lions

trees and parks

people working

boys playing

big buildings

big airport

big trucks

animal tracks

new homes

men helping machines work

What Machine Is This?

What Machine Is Like This?

Imagine

" I want to sleep, " said Mr. Big.
" Go away and let me sleep. "

Did the animals go away?
No, they did not.

The goat said, " Ma-a-a! "
The duck said, " Quack! Quack! "
The cow said, " Moo-oo! Moo-oo! "

Mr. Big said, " I can't sleep here.
But I know what I can do.
I can go to the city. Now! "

The animals saw Mr. Big go away.
" Ma-a-a! Ma-a-a! " said the goat.
" Quack! Quack! " said the duck.
" Moo-oo! Moo-oo! " said the cow.

Away went Mr. Big.

"I can see the new buildings," he said.

"I can walk up the streets and down the streets.

I can walk in the park.

And I can go to sleep in the city too."

Mr. Big saw some new buildings.
He went up and down the streets.
And he went for a walk in the park.

"Now I want to sleep," said Mr. Big.
"My animals can't stop me
from going to sleep in the city."

Did Mr. Big go to sleep?
No, he did not.

"Who can sleep in this city?"
he asked. "I can't!
Not with cars going up and down
the streets all the time.
The cars come and go,
and they don't stop."

Mr. Big said, " I'm going home.
I'm going home now."
And away he went.

At home the animals ran to Mr. Big.
But Mr. Big didn't stop.

"I'm going to sleep," he said. "Now!"

The goat said, "Ma-a-a! Ma-a-a!"
The duck said, "Quack! Quack!"
The cow said, "Moo-oo! Moo-oo!"

Did Mr. Big get up?
No, he did not.
Mr. Big went to sleep.

Carlo

Carlo looked down the street.

He said, " Mr. Bell is sleeping.
I'm going to the park.
Mr. Bell is in bed,
and he can't stop me. "

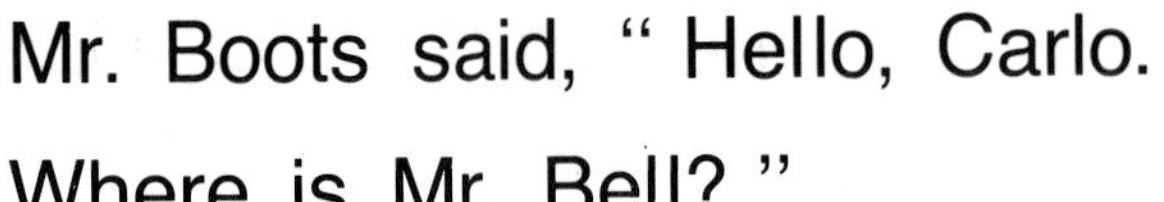

Mr. Boots said, " Hello, Carlo.
Where is Mr. Bell? "

Carlo went on.
Away he ran.

Mr. Boots said, " Stop, Carlo!
Don't run away.
You'll get lost. "

But Carlo didn't stop.

A woman said, " Hello, Carlo.
Here's something for you. "

Carlo ran on.
He ran and ran.

" Stop, Carlo! Stop! " said the woman.
" Don't run away. "

But Carlo didn't stop.

" Get out of the street! "
said a man.

" Get out!
You can't run here.
Get out of the street fast. "

Carlo ran to the park.
He did not stop.

" This is fun, " said Carlo.

" I'm going to eat in the park. "

A man looked up.

He said, " You can't eat here.

Go away! "

Carlo ran away from the man.

He ran to a tree, and up he jumped.

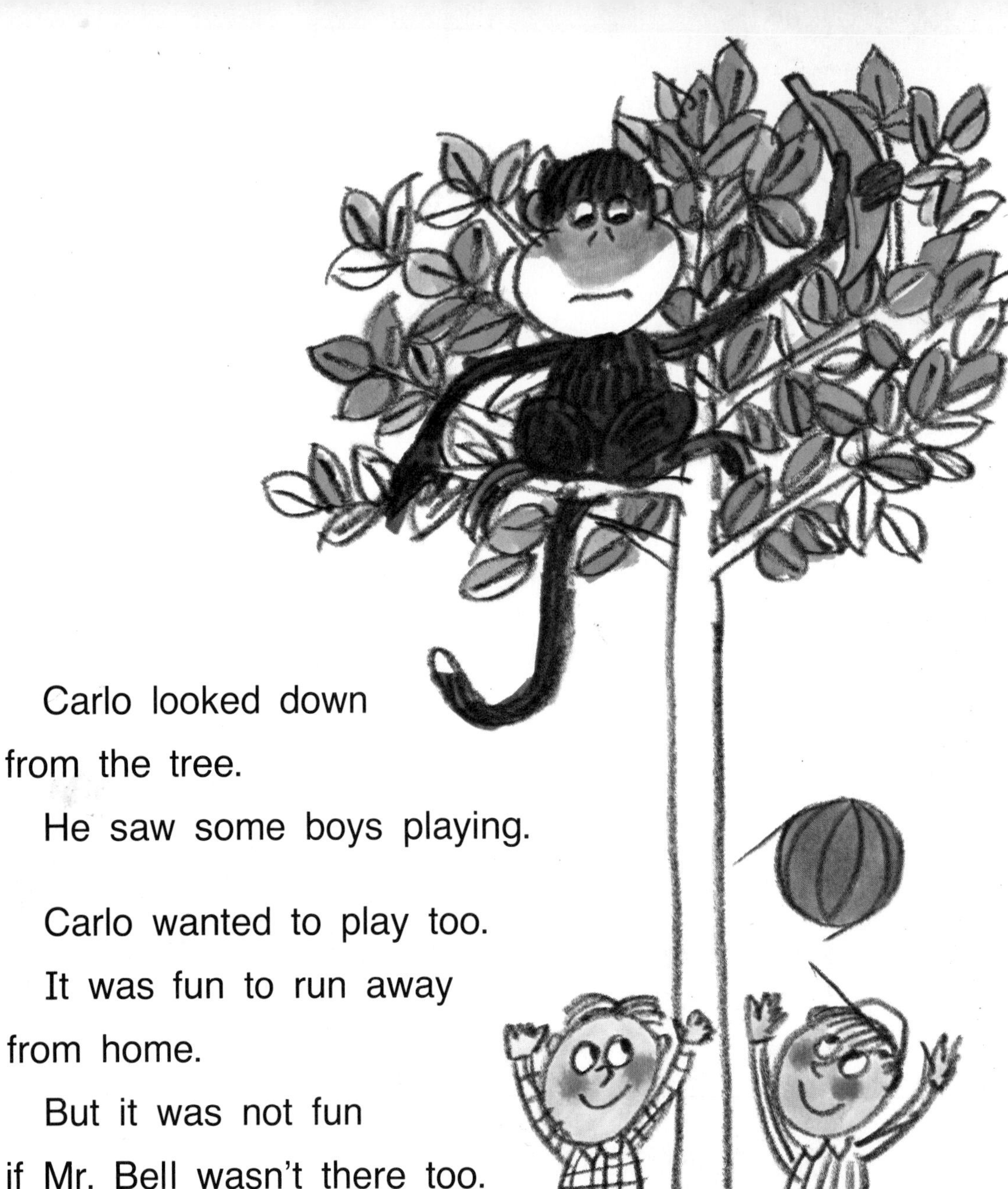

Carlo looked down
from the tree.

He saw some boys playing.

Carlo wanted to play too.

It was fun to run away
from home.

But it was not fun
if Mr. Bell wasn't there too.

Mr. Bell was not in bed.
He was in the park
looking for Carlo.

Mr. Bell looked up
and said, "Carlo!
What are you doing
in the tree?
What are you doing up there?
You come down."

And Carlo did. He jumped.
He jumped down on Mr. Bell.
And away they went.

Jennifer Likes to Imagine Things

" I like to imagine things, "
Jennifer said.

When I see a leaf,
I say, " That leaf is a ship.
And I'm little.
I'm going for a ride on that ship.
I'm on that ship
and I'm going away—away—away. "

When I see a falling star,
I say, " That's a space ship.
I imagine that falling star is
a space ship.
I'm on that star
and it's falling—falling—falling.
That ship was out in space,
but now it has come home."

It's fun to imagine things.

I see a cat with yellow eyes.
When I see that cat,
I say, " That's a lion.
A lion with yellow, yellow eyes.
Here he comes! Help! Help! "

"And here he is *NOW!*"
said Jennifer.

"Imagine that!"

Let's Imagine Funny Things

What funny things do you see here?

Can you imagine
a hen with a pen?
a cat who can bat?
a pig with a wig?

What funny things can you think of?
a fox in a ________?
a goat in a ________?
a ________ with a ________?

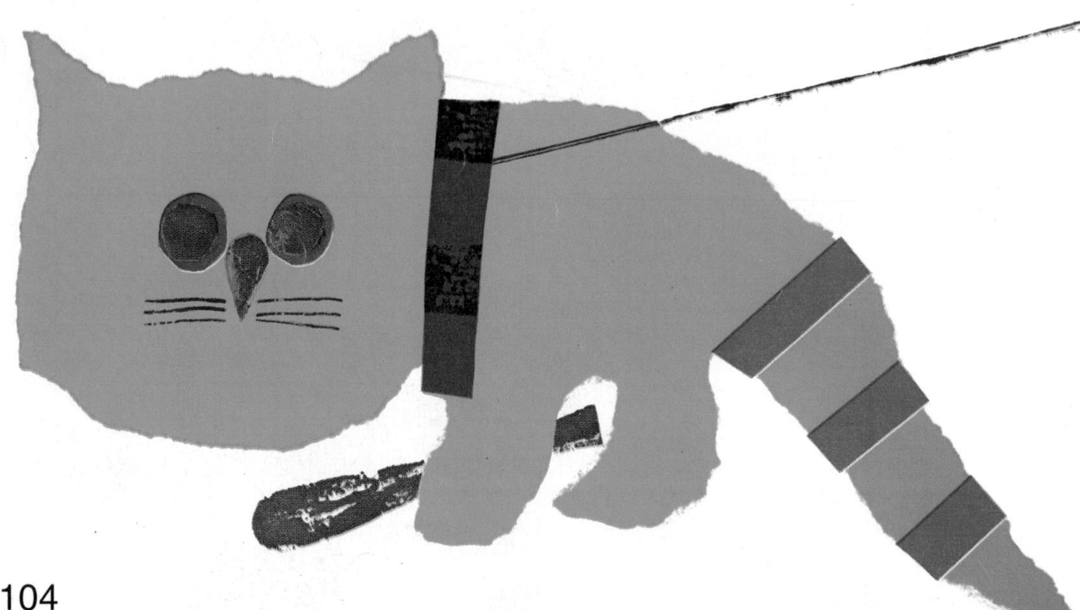

Mr. Pine's Signs

Mr. Pine made signs.

Mr. Pine made all of the signs in Little Town.
He made signs for the streets.
And he made signs for the buildings.

The people in Little Town
liked the signs Mr. Pine made.

But the signs in Little Town got old—
too old for people to read.

The Mayor said, " I will ask Mr. Pine
to put up some new signs. "

The Mayor went
to Mr. Pine's house.

"The signs are too old for people to read," said the Mayor.

"Will you make new signs for Little Town?"

"Yes, I will," said Mr. Pine.

The Mayor went home, and Mr. Pine went to work.

Mr. Pine made red signs, and green signs, and yellow signs.

He made red signs for Stop and green signs for Park.

And he made yellow signs for Hill Street.

“Now the signs are all made,”
said Mr. Pine.
“And I’m going to sleep.”

Mr. Pine got up.

" Now where did I put my glasses? " he said.

Mr. Pine looked everywhere in the house.

" That's funny! " he said.

" I don't know where my glasses are. "

Mr. Pine
looked here.

And here.

And here.

" I can't stop to find my glasses, "
said Mr. Pine.
" I have to put up the new signs. "

He got the signs
and went out of the house.

The Mixed-Up Signs

Mr. Pine put up the signs in Little Town.

He didn't know
they were mixed up.

But they were!

The signs were mixed up everywhere.

A man said, " What is this? "

A woman said, " Who did this? "

The Mayor said, " Find Mr. Pine. Fast!
The signs have to be fixed. "

Mr. Pine was at home.

" All the signs are up, "
said Mr. Pine.
" And I can look for my glasses.
Now where are they? "

He looked and looked.

" Did I put my glasses in here? "
he asked.

Mr. Pine looked in the dog house.
He said, " My glasses!
Here they are. "

Mr. Pine put the glasses on
and went to see the signs.

This is what Mr. Pine saw.

" Oh, my! " said Mr. Pine.

" My signs are all mixed up. "

" Mr. Pine! " said the Mayor.

" Do something! The signs have to be fixed. "

Mr. Pine went to work and fixed the signs.

He fixed all the signs in Little Town.

Then Mr. Pine went home.

" The signs are fixed, " he said.

" And that's that! "

About the Teeth of Sharks

The thing about a shark is—teeth,
One row above, one row beneath.

Now take a close look. Do you find
It has another row behind?

Still closer—here, I'll hold your hat:
Has it a third row behind that?

Now look in and . . . Look out! Oh my,
I'll *never* know now! Well, goodbye.

John Ciardi

Say the Words
and Walk Up
way
sack
tray
pack
say
back
Ray
take
play
trick
rake
pay
quick
make
may
lake
Kay
cake
hay
bake
day

What's Mixed Up?

Fly Away

Hide and Seek

Suzu and Liz and Ben and Pete were playing hide and seek.

Suzu was It.

" 1, 2, 3, 4, 5, 6, . . . "

Liz hid in back of a box.
Pete hid in the weeds.
Ben hid up in a tree.

" Here I come! " Suzu said.

When Suzu looked up in the tree, she didn't see Ben.

But she did see a little bird looking down at her.

When Suzu looked in the weeds, she didn't see Pete.

But she did see a big yellow butterfly.

Ben came down from the tree.

" You didn't find me, " he said.

But Suzu didn't look at Ben.

Liz was in back of the box,
but Suzu didn't see Liz.

" Guess what Mr. Hill has here! "
said Suzu.

" A box of kittens, " Ben said.

" 1, 2, 3, 4, 5, " Suzu said.
" Five little kittens. "

sik

"I *do* like to play hide and seek," Suzu said.

"When you play hide and seek, you can find surprises.

And surprises like this are fun!"

Kittens

" Look at this sign! " Suzu said.

Liz and Ben and Pete came to look.

" Is Mr. Hill going to sell the kittens? " asked Liz.

Mr. Hill came out.

" No, I'm not, " he said.

" I'm going to find good homes for the kittens.

Who wants a kitten? "

"Oh, I want one," said Suzu.
"It will have a good home
with me."

"Me too," Pete said.

"I want a kitten," Ben said.

"I want a little kitten too," said Liz.

"Good," said Mr. Hill.
"You all go home
and ask if you can have a kitten."

Suzu and Ben and Pete and Liz
ran home.

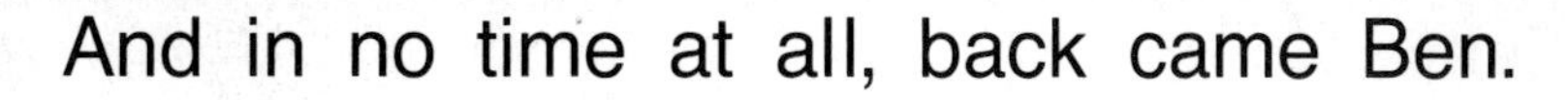

And in no time at all, back came Ben.
" I can have a kitten, " he said.

" O.K., " Mr. Hill said.
" They are all alike. Take one. "

" I want this kitten, " Ben said.
" It has big feet. "

Liz and Pete came back.
" Pete can have one
and I can too, " said Liz.

" Take one, " Mr. Hill said.

" This is the kitten I want, " said Liz.
" It has little feet. "

" And here is the one I want, "
said Pete.
" This one has big ears. "

Suzu came too.

" Take one, " said Mr. Hill.

" This is the kitten I wanted all the time, " Suzu said.

" It has little ears. "

" The kittens all looked alike to me, "
Mr. Hill said.
" But they don't look alike to you, do they? "

" No, " Suzu said.
" They aren't alike. "

" Me-ow, Me-ow, Me-ow. "

" That's my kitten, " Mr. Hill said.

" It has a big Me-ow, " said Suzu.

" Good! " said Mr. Hill.
" Kittens aren't alike at all, are they?
Now I know. "

Quickly fly away
Into the mist
My bird—
You are free!

Issa

Quick as a Grasshopper

Dimity didn't like to walk.

Dimity ran.

She ran in the house
and she ran out of the house.

" Slow down, Dimity, " her big sister said.

" Don't go so fast.

Slow down, Dimity. "

So Dimity did.

" Dimity, " her big sister said.

" Will you run down the street
and get a newspaper for me? "

So Dimity ran.

Out in the street,
Mr. Fell was walking his dog.

Mr. Mack and his little boy
were going down the street too.
The boy had a big ball.

" That's a big ball for a little boy, "
Mr. Mack said.
" Let me have it.
You can have it after we get home. "

The boy said, " No. "
And Mr. Mack said, " Yes. "
And away went the ball.

With a jump—Dimity went after it.
" Here you are! " she said.

" My, my, " said Mr. Fell.
" Dimity, you're as quick as a grasshopper. "

Just then, a cat went down the street.

Mr. Fell's dog went after the cat.
Dimity went after the dog.
And Mr. Fell went after Dimity.

With a jump and a hop,
Dimity had the dog.
"Here you are!" she said to Mr. Fell.

"My, my, Dimity," Mr. Fell said.
"You're as quick as a grasshopper."

Dimity ran to the store.

She got the newspaper,
and ran home with it.

" Slow down Dimity. Don't go so fast, "
her big sister said.
" Slow down! "

" O.K., " said Dimity.
" I'll slow down. "

And she did.

Dimity went out of the house.
This time, she didn't run.
She sat down on the walk.

She looked and looked.
And she saw something.
Hop—it jumped away!

"A grasshopper!" said Dimity.

So Dimity jumped up.
And she went back in the house.
—as *quick* as a grasshopper.

"Guess what I saw,"
she said to her sister.
"Guess what I saw!"

Bozo

Mike wanted a dog.

" This house is too little for a dog, " said Mother.

" But I have a name for a dog, " said Mike.

" I'll name my dog Bozo. "

" No, Mike, " said Mother.

" This house is too little for a dog. "

Mike saw a frog in the park.
He wanted Mother to see it too.

Mike ran home with the frog.
He said, " Look, Mother.
I got this frog in the park.
I'll name it Bozo the Frog. "

Mother said,
" Let's not have a frog
in the house, Mike. "

Mike went out of the house with the frog.
He saw a boy with a mouse.

Mike said, " Let me have the mouse.
And I will let you have this frog. "

The boy went away with the frog.
And Mike ran home with the mouse.

" A boy let me have this mouse, " said Mike.

" See what it can do. "

Mother said, " I don't want a mouse in the house. "

" Bozo is a good name for a mouse, " said Mike.

" This mouse likes the name Bozo. It's just a little mouse. "

" No, Mike, " said Mother.

Mike ran to the pet store.

He saw some ants in a box.

" Mother will not let me have this mouse, " said Mike.

" Do you want it for the pet store, Mr. Park? "

" Yes, I do, " said Mr. Park.

" Let me have the mouse.

And you may have the ants. "

" Thank you, " said Mike.

Mike ran home from the pet store.

He wanted Mother to see the ants.

" I let Mr. Park have the mouse, " said Mike.

" And he let me have some ants. "

" No ants, Mike, " said Mother.

" They can't get out of the box, " said Mike.

But Mother said, " No. "

" Oh, Mother, " said Mike.

" I want a pet.

I just have to have a pet. "

" You *do* want a pet, don't you? "
asked Mother.

" I guess we can get a pet
for you.

And I know just the pet you'll like.

Do you want a *little* dog? "

" I saw a little dog in the pet store, "
said Mike.

" I do want a dog, Mother. "

Mother and Mike went to the store.
They saw the little dog.

Mike said, " Come here, Bozo. "

" We will take this dog, "
said Mother.
" Bozo will make a good pet for Mike. "

" He came to me! " said Mike.
" He likes the name Bozo. "

Let's Have Fun
1,
2,
3,
4,
5.
Here I come!
Two to turn
and one to jump.
And now,
I'll read
a story.

Let's play!
O.K.
Look what
I made!
It's a hit!

The Secret

Anna said, " I'd like to have
a little bird house.

I'd put it in the tree,
and I'd put food in it
for the little birds.

Maybe I'd see a bird eating there. "

" Maybe I'll get a bird house for you, "
her mother said.

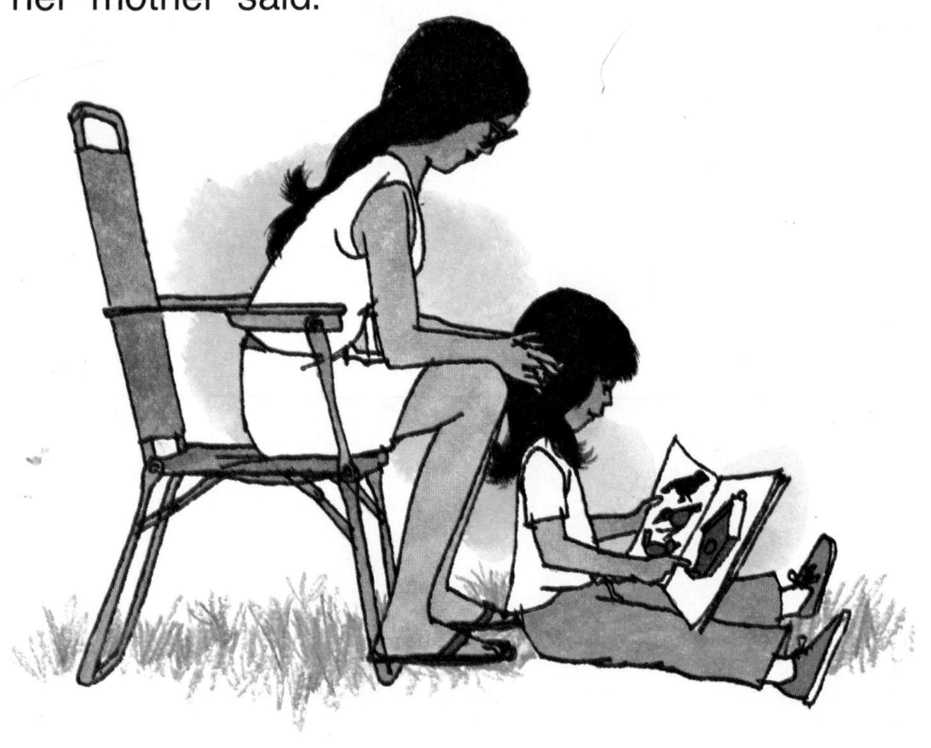

Anna said to Ben,
" I have a secret. "

" What's the secret? " Ben asked.

" Maybe I'm going to get a little bird house, " Anna said.

" I'd like to have a bird house too, " said Ben.

Ben said to Tim,
" I have a secret.
Anna's going to get a bird house. "

" What's she going to put in it? "
asked Tim.

" Maybe a parrot, " said Ben.

" I'd like to have a parrot too, "
said Tim.

Tim said to Emily,
" I have a secret. "

" What's the secret? "
Emily asked.

" Anna's got a parrot—a big parrot.
Maybe it can talk, " said Tim.

" A parrot can talk! " Emily said.
"*All* parrots can talk. "

Emily said to Pat,

" I have a secret.

Anna's got a big purple parrot.

And it can talk. "

" What can it say? " Pat asked.

" I don't know, " said Emily.

" That's a funny thing for a parrot to say, " said Pat.

Pat said to Dimity,

“ Anna’s got a funny purple parrot.
A big purple parrot.
It can talk.
It can say ‘ I-don’t-know. ’ ”

“ Let’s all go to Anna’s house and see that parrot, ” said Dimity.

So they all went to Anna's house!

And look what they saw!

BIRD
SEED

Pets

Is it a good pet?

Why or why not?

What's on the Line?

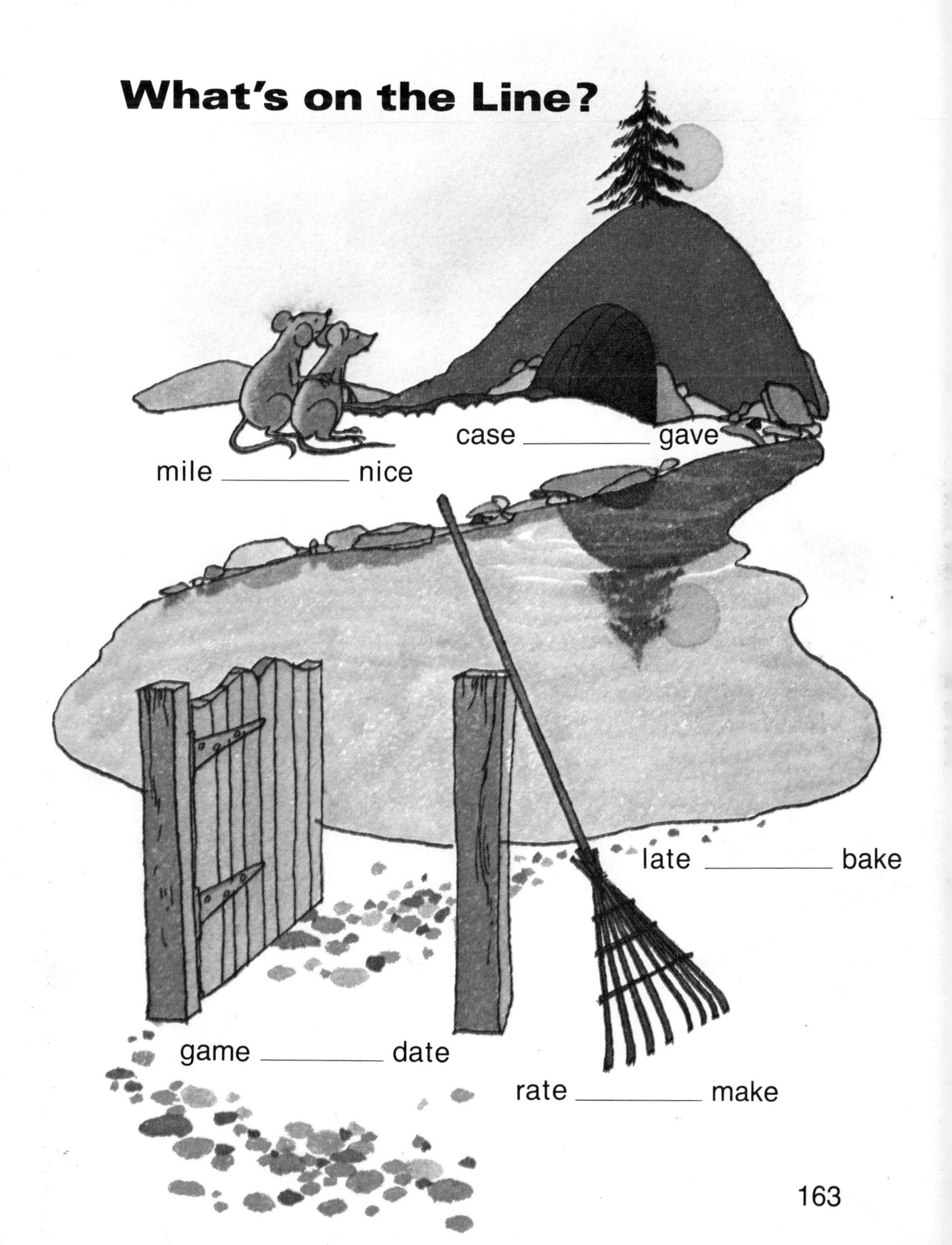

case __________ gave

mile __________ nice

late __________ bake

game __________ date

rate __________ make

Old Tales to Tell

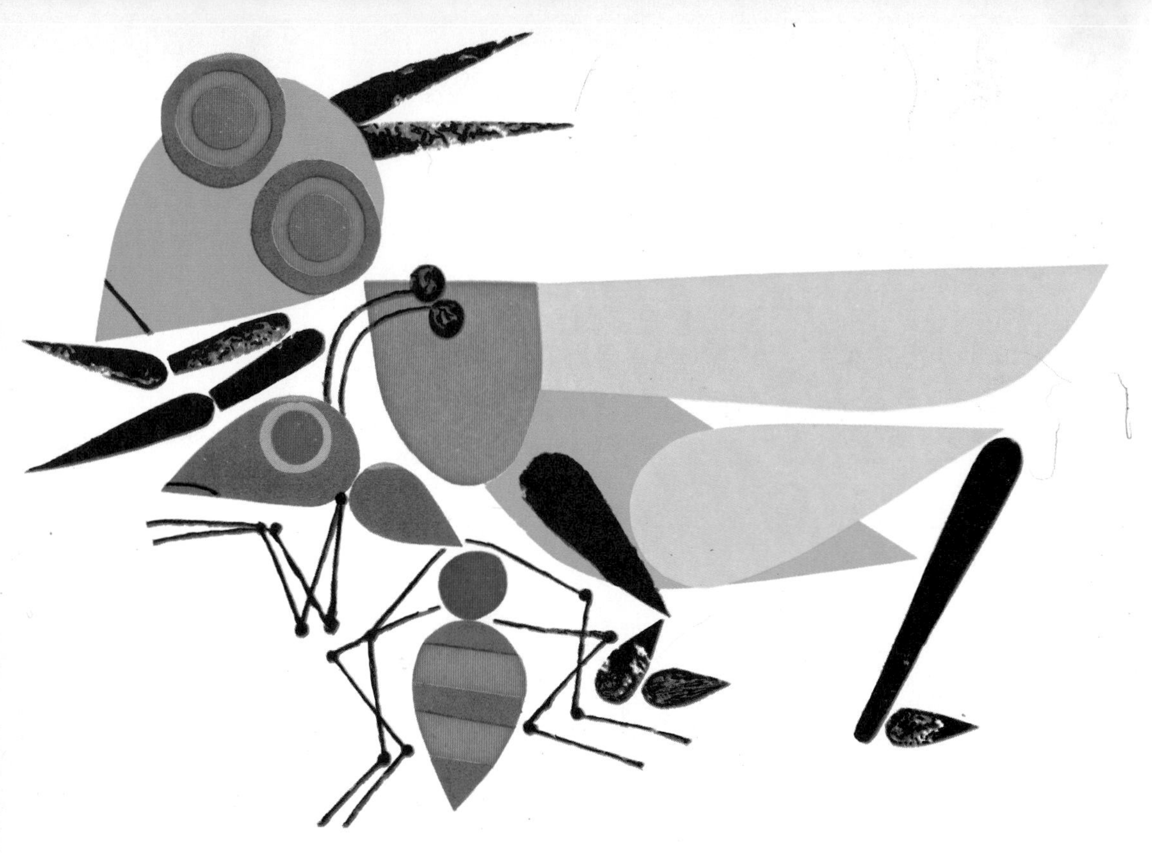

The Ant and the Grasshopper

" Hello, Little Ant, " said a grasshopper.
" Will you come and play with me?
I will hide in the grass,
and you can look for me there. "

The ant said, " You can hide
in the grass.
But I can't look for you there.
I have work to do. "

" Don't work, " said the grasshopper.

" When do you play, Little Ant? "

" I don't have time to play, "
said the ant.

" I'm looking for food.
I'm going to put the food away.
And when the snow comes,
I will have food to eat. "

" Work away! " said the grasshopper.
" I'm going to play now. "
And away he went in the grass.

The ant went on working.
" You can play,
but I will work, " the ant said.
" And I will have food to eat
when the snow comes. "

The snow came.

Down,

down

it came.

The grasshopper saw the snow.
" What am I going to do? " he said.
" I can't play now.
I want some food, but what can I eat? "

The ant saw the grasshopper in the snow.

" What are you doing there? "
the ant asked.

" Are you looking for something? "

" Yes I am, " said the grasshopper.

" I'm looking for you.
Help me, Little Ant.
Let me have something to eat. "

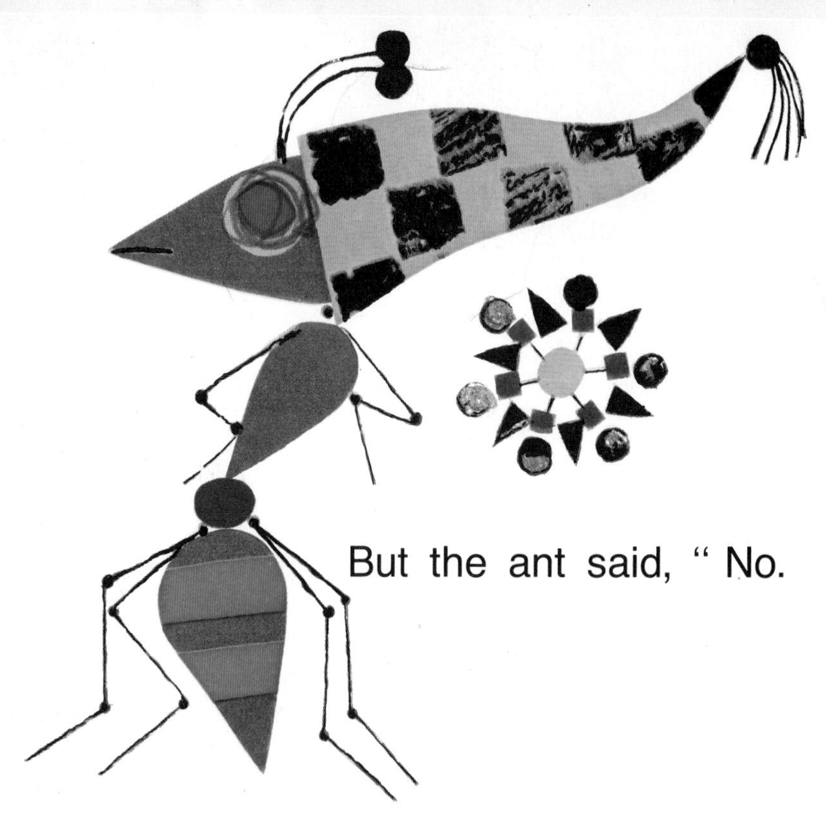

But the ant said, " No.

You played when I worked.
You didn't work, Grasshopper. "
And away went the ant.

" Stop! " called the grasshopper.
" Don't go away. "
He called and called,
but the ant still did not stop.

And the grasshopper walked away.
On and on he went in the snow.

In the Country

The city mouse wanted to see the country mouse.

" I know what I can do, " he said. " I'm going to the country. I will surprise Country Mouse. "

Away went the city mouse. He ran and ran, and at last he came to the country.

City Mouse called,
" Country Mouse! Where are you? "

" Here I am, " said Country Mouse.
" Did you come to see me? "

City Mouse said, " Yes, I did.
I ran all the way from the city.
And at last I'm here. "

" What can I do for you? "
asked Country Mouse.

" Can I have some food? "
asked City Mouse.

" I did not find a thing to eat
on the way. "

Country Mouse said, " Follow me,
and we will get something to eat. "

Then away went Country Mouse.
And away went City Mouse.

Country Mouse said, " Here we are at last!
Eat away, City Mouse. "

City Mouse wanted to eat.
But he did not like the food.

" You are not eating, "
said Country Mouse.
" Why don't you eat with me? "

" I can't, " said City Mouse.
" I don't like this food.
Why do you eat it, Country Mouse? "

Country Mouse looked surprised.
He said, "This is all the food I have.
When a mouse lives in the country,
he eats country food."

"Why do you live in the country?"
asked City Mouse.
"Why don't you come home with me?
I know you will like city food."

"I don't know the way,"
said Country Mouse.
"But I will follow you."

Then away they went.

In the City

City Mouse and Country Mouse
ran up hill and down hill.

At last they were in the city.

" I know where we can get some food, "
said City Mouse.
" Follow me. "

" I will, " said Country Mouse.

" At last we are here, "
said City Mouse.
" We will go into this house.
The people will be in bed. "

" Do people live here? "
asked Country Mouse.
" I don't like people! "

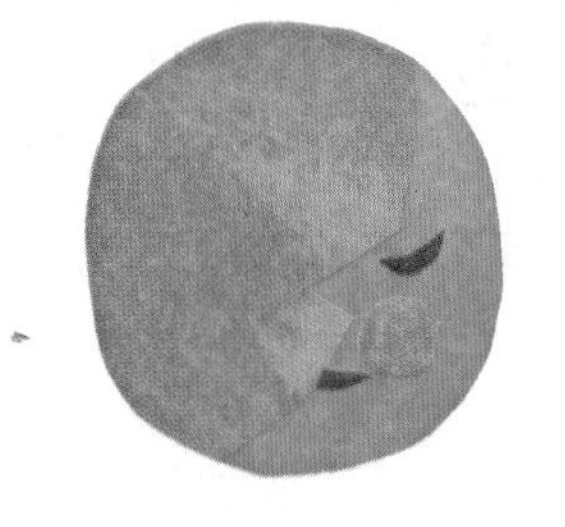

City Mouse said,
" The people are in bed.
They can't see you.
Come with me. "
And he went into the house.

Country Mouse went into the house too.
He looked for City Mouse,
and he called, " Where are you? "

" Here I am, " said City Mouse.
" Jump up here with me. "

When Country Mouse jumped,
he saw some food.

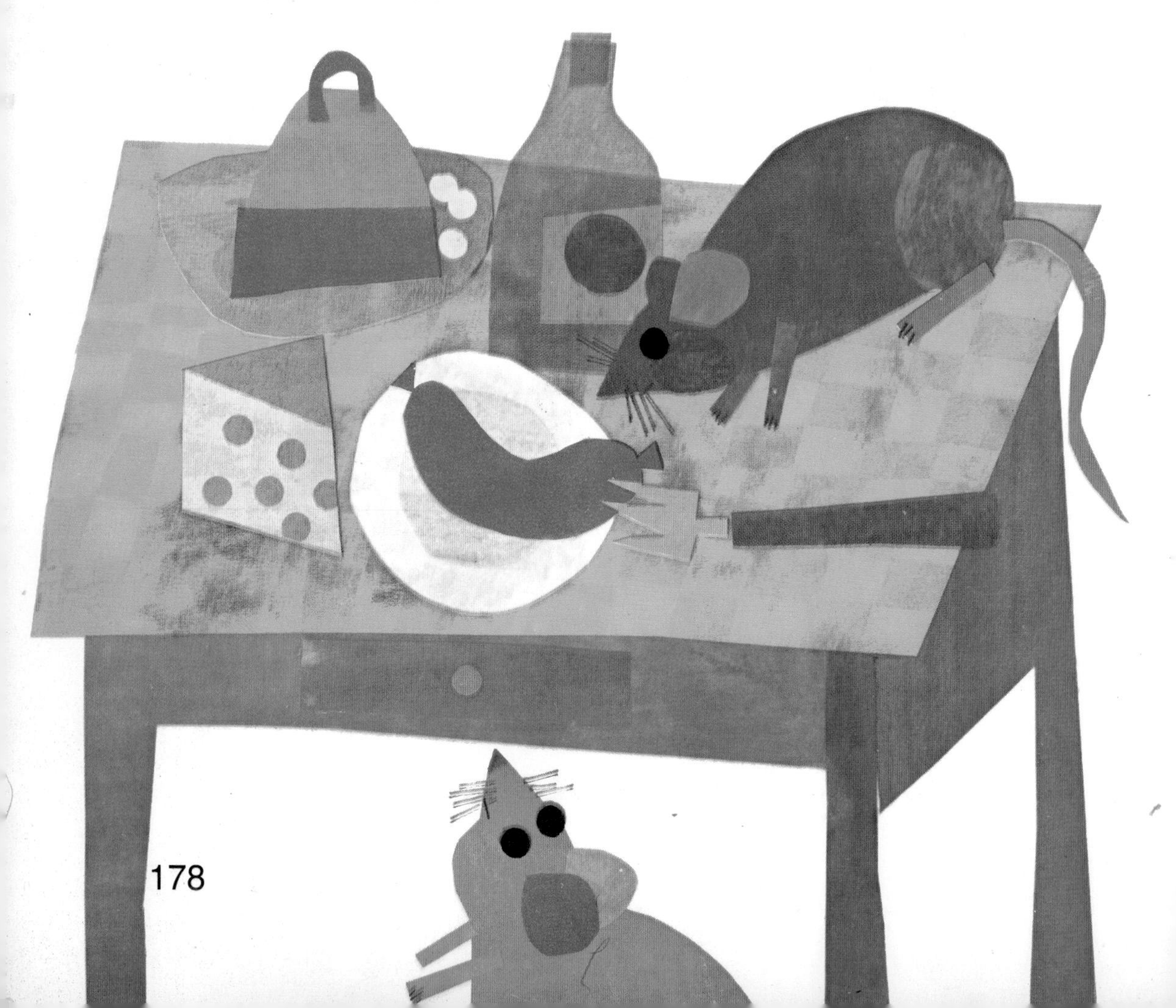

" Eat away! " said City Mouse.
" You will like this food. "

Country Mouse said, " I do like it.
I may not go back to the country. "

City Mouse said, " Don't go back!
You can live here with me. "

When they were eating,
City Mouse saw something big.
He said, " Run! Run, Country Mouse.
And don't stop. "

Away went City Mouse.
And away went Country Mouse.
They ran out of the house.

City Mouse called, " Come back, Country Mouse!

There is no danger now.

The cat went back into the house. "

But Country Mouse did not stop.

He called, " No, I don't like to live where there is danger.

I'm going home. "

Country Mouse ran up a hill
and into the country.

When he got home, he said,
"At last I can stop!
I will not go back to the city.
Not where the cat is!
I will eat country food,
and City Mouse can live in danger."

THE THREE BILLY GOATS GRUFF

Once there were three billy goats,
and the name of the three goats was Gruff.

There was Little Billy Goat Gruff,

and Big Billy Goat Gruff.

And Big, Big Billy Goat Gruff.

The three Billy Goats Gruff went up the hill.

They wanted to eat some green grass.

But on the way up was a bridge.

And under the bridge lived a troll— a big,

old

troll.

Little Billy Goat Gruff
walked on the bridge.

Trip, trap! Trip, trap!

went the bridge.

" Who's that walking on my bridge? "
asked the troll.

" It is I, Little Billy Goat Gruff.
I'm going up the hill to eat
some green grass, " said the little goat.

" You can't walk on my bridge, "
said the troll.

" I'm going to eat you up! "

Little Billy Goat Gruff said,
" Oh, no! Don't eat me.
I'm just a little billy goat.
Wait for Big Billy Goat. "

The troll did wait
for Big Billy Goat.

Then Big Billy Goat walked on the bridge.

Trip, trap! Trip, trap!

went the bridge.

" Who's that walking on my bridge? "
asked the troll.

" It is I, Big Billy Goat Gruff.
I'm going up the hill to eat
some green grass, " said the big billy goat.

"You can't walk on my bridge," said the troll.

"I'm going to eat you up!"

Big Billy Goat Gruff said, "Oh, no! Don't eat me.
I'm just a big billy goat.
Wait for Big, Big Billy Goat."

The troll did wait for Big, Big Billy Goat.

Then Big, Big Billy Goat Gruff
walked on the bridge.

Trip, trap! Trip, trap! Trip, trap!

went the bridge.

" Who's that walking on my bridge? "
asked the troll.

" It is I! " said the big, big billy goat.

" I'm going to eat you! "
said the troll.
" **You** are the goat
I want. "

Then up
on the bridge
went the troll.

He ran at
Big, Big Billy Goat.

But Big, Big Billy Goat
ran at the troll.

And down went the troll
from the bridge. Down,

down,

down.

Now the three billy goats
go up the hill to eat grass.

And there is no old troll
under the bridge.

Henny Penny

Henny Penny was eating her food
when—*PLOP*—
something fell on her tail.

"Oh my," said Henny Penny.
"The sky is falling.
A bit of it fell on my tail.
I will go and tell the king."

She went on her way.
And on the way, she met a duck.

"Where are you going, Henny Penny?"
asked the duck.

"I'm going to tell the king
the sky is falling," said Henny Penny.
"A bit of it fell on my tail."

"May I go with you?" asked the duck.

"Certainly," said Henny Penny.

They went on.

And on the way, they met a rabbit.

" Where are you going? "
asked the rabbit.

" We are going to find the king, "
said Henny Penny.

" We are going to tell him
that the sky is falling.
A bit of it fell on my tail. "

" May I go with you? "
asked the rabbit.

" Certainly, " said Henny Penny.

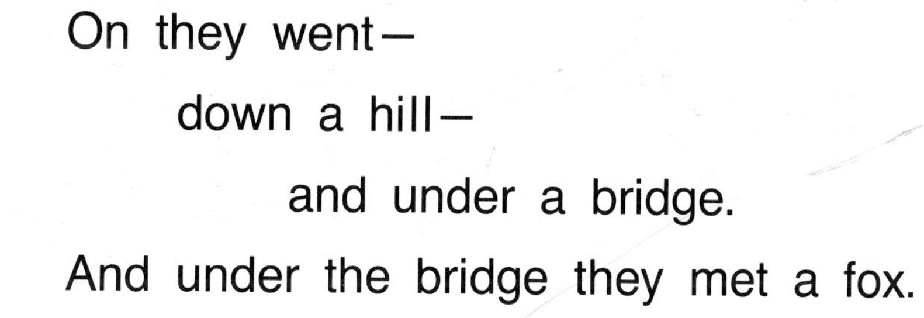

On they went—

down a hill—

and under a bridge.

And under the bridge they met a fox.

The fox said to Henny Penny, "Where are you going?"

"We are going to tell the king the sky is falling. A bit of it fell on my tail," said Henny Penny.

"I know the way," the fox said. "I will help you find the king. Follow me."

"Certainly," said Henny Penny.

On the way, they came
to the fox's den.

"Let's stop here," the fox said.
"Come in. Come in
one at a time."

And the fox went into his den.

The rabbit went in after him.
But the rabbit was too quick for the fox.
The rabbit ran out.

" Henny Penny! " the rabbit said.
" The fox wanted to eat me! *RUN!*
Run, Duck! Run, Henny Penny! "

So the rabbit and the duck
and Henny Penny ran.

They ran all the way home.

And Henny Penny never did tell
the king that the sky was falling.

Stories We Like to Read

Henny Penny
The Three Little Pigs
The Little Red Hen

Can You Tell a New Tale?

"Hello, Little Ant," said a grasshopper.
"Will you come and play with me?"

The ant said, "Yes, I will play.
I do not like to work."

A fox met Henny Penny, a duck and a rabbit.

"Do you want to come to see the king?"
asked Henny Penny.

"No," said the fox. "I'll wait till you come back."

"Who's that walking on my bridge?"
asked the troll.

"It is I, Little Billy Goat Gruff.
I'm going up the hill to eat some green grass,"
said the little goat.

"Wait, I'll go with you," said the troll.

This and That

I like
a little of this
and
a little of that.

I like
the garden path
red balloons
purple grapes
a good bath.

I like
wooly sheep
green grass
blue sky
good sleep.

I like
a little of this
and
a little of that.

What do you like?

Home for a Bunny

" Spring, Spring, Spring! "
sang the robin.

" Spring, Spring, Spring! "
sang the frog.

" Spring! "
said the groundhog.

It was Spring.

In the Spring a bunny
came down the road.
He was going to find
a home of his own.
A home for a bunny,
A home of his own,
Under a rock,
Under a stone,
Under a log,
Or under the ground.
Where would a bunny find a home?

" Where is your home? "
he asked the robin.

"Here, here, here,"
sang the robin.
"Here in this nest is my home."

"Here, here, here,"
sang the little robins.
"Here is our home."

"Not for me," said the bunny.
"I would fall out of a nest.
I would fall on the ground."

So he went on looking for a home.

" Where is your home? "
he asked the frog.

"Wog, wog, wog,"
sang the frog.
"Wog, wog, wog,
Under the water,
Down in the bog."

"Not for me,"
said the bunny.
"Under the water,
I would drown in a bog."

So he went on
looking for a home.

"Where do you live?"
he asked the groundhog.

" In a log, "
said the groundhog.

" May I come in? "
said the bunny.

" No, you can't come in my log, "
said the groundhog.

So the bunny went down the road.

Down the road
and down the road he went.

He was going to find
a home of his own.

A home for a bunny,
A home of his own,
Under a rock
Or a log
Or a stone.

Where would a bunny find a home?

Down the road
and down the road
and down the road
he went, until—

He met a bunny.

"Where is your home?"
he asked the bunny.

“ Here, ” said the bunny.
“ Here is my home.
Under this rock,
Under this stone,
Down under the ground,
Here is my home. ”

"May I come in?"
said the bunny.

"Yes," said the bunny.

And so he did.

And that was his home.

New Words in This Book

The following new words are presented in *May I Come In?*, Level 5, Reading 720. Words printed in regular type are new basic words. Those underlined are enrichment words, and those printed in color are new words that pupils can decode independently.

UNIT 1

PAGE

8 looking
9 bit
of
leaf
weed
comes
gets
10 near
log
sees
11 under
13 fine
hen
16 snowman
tree
creeping
snow
he's
food
17 find
bite
19 boy
22 bits
eats
23 sits
washes
his
face
feet
24 raccoons
live
home
raccoon
25 now
follow
down
26 up
27 tracks
know
28 on
30 made
31 homes
32 danger
squirrel
34 den
35 snake

UNIT 2

46 new
boots
James
have
48 looked
49 Penny
aren't
need
50 balloon
thank
51 red
my
52 went
52 didn't
where
her
going
53 Jet
54 wants
she's

55 asked
57 saw
oh
58 some
balloons
may
59 purple
60 pigeons
popcorn
Toni
buildings
came
street
lost
sister
meet
62 Mike
eating
fell
67 bag
68 Isabel
David
Yee
be
surprises
all
69 Pete
Ken
Dan
that
building
70 fire
truck
fighter
71 then
everywhere
72 try
hat
73 seems
76 back
78 work
machines

UNIT 3

86 Mr.
sleep
goat
Ma-a-a
quack
cow
Moo-oo
87 city
88 walk
streets
90 cars
93 Carlo
Bell
bed
96 out
97 fun
jumped
98 playing
wanted
was
if
there
99 doing
100 Jennifer
imagine
things
when
ship
101 falling
star
that's
space
has
102 cat
yellow
eyes
104 pen
bat
pig
wig
think
106 Pine's
signs
Pine
town
107 people
liked
got
Mayor
ask

107 put
house
108 green
110 glasses
113 mixed
were
115 fixed

UNIT 4

126 seek
Suzu
Liz
hid
weeds
box

127 bird
128 butterfly
129 kittens
five
131 sign
sell
good
kitten
132 one
133 alike
take
ears
135 meow
137 quick
grasshopper
Dimity
slow
so
newspaper
138 walking
had
139 after
jump
142 store
sat
144 Bozo
name
145 frog
147 just
148 pet
store
ants
152 two
turn
153 story
hit
154 secret
Anna
I'd
bird
maybe
156 Tim
157 Emily
talk
parrots
158 Pat
thing

UNIT 5

166 ant
grass
170 played
worked
called
171 country
last
172 way
174 why
175 lives
177 into
181 danger
183 Billy
Gruff
once
184 bridge
lived
troll
185 trap
186 wait
192 Henny
plop
tail
sky
tell
king
193 met
certainly
199 never
200 stories

EFGHIJK 7987
PRINTED IN THE UNITED STATES OF AMERICA